SELECTED FROM

CHINA MEN DISCARDED

& THE WOMAN WARRIOR

Maxine
Hong
Kingston

WRITERS' VOICES

SIGNAL HILL

ATTENTION READERS: We would like to hear what you think about our books. Please send your comments or suggestions to:

Signal Hill Publications
P.O. Box 131
Syracuse, NY 13210-0131

•   •   •

Additional material
© 1990 Signal Hill Publications
A publishing imprint of Laubach Literacy International

10   9   8   7   6   5   4   3   2

First printing: April 1990

ISBN 0-929631-12-9

The words "Writers' Voices" are a trademark of Signal Hill Publications.

Cover designed by Paul Davis Studio
Interior designed by Barbara Huntley

Signal Hill is a not-for-profit publisher. The proceeds from the sale of this book support the national and international programs of Laubach Literacy International.

This book was printed on 100% recycled paper which contains 50% post-consumer waste.

Acknowledgments

We gratefully acknowledge the generous support of the following foundations and corporations that made the publication of WRITERS' VOICES and NEW WRITERS' VOICES possible: The Vincent Astor Foundation; Booth Ferris Foundation; Exxon Corporation; James Money Management, Inc.; Knight Foundation; Philip Morris Companies Inc.; Scripps Howard Foundation; Uris Brothers Foundation, Inc.; The H.W. Wilson Foundation; and Weil, Gotshal & Manges Foundation Inc.

This book could not have been realized without the kind and generous cooperation of the author, Maxine Hong Kingston, and her publisher, Alfred A. Knopf, Inc.

We deeply appreciate the contributions of the following suppliers: Cam Steel Die Rule Works Inc. (steel cutting die for display); Canadian Pacific Forest Products Ltd. (text stock); Creative Graphics, Inc. (text typesetting); Horizon Paper Co., Inc. (cover stock); Martin/Friess Communications (display header); Mergenthaler Container (corrugated display); Phototype Color Graphics (cover color separations); and Ringier America Dresden Division (cover and text printing and binding).

Our thanks to Paul Davis Studio and Myrna Davis, Paul Davis, and Jeanine Esposito for their inspired design of the covers of WRITERS' VOICES. Thanks also to Barbara Huntley for her sensitive attention to the interior design of this series.

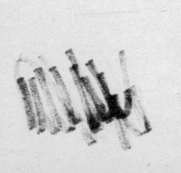

CONTENTS

ABOUT *WRITERS' VOICES*

"I want to read what others do—what I see people reading in libraries, on the subway, and at home."

> Mamie Moore, a literacy student,
> Brooklyn, New York

Writers' Voices is our response to Mamie Moore's wish:

- the wish to step forward into the reading community,
- the wish to have access to new information,
- the wish to read to her grandchildren,
- the wish to read for the joy of reading.

NOTE TO THE READER

"What we are familiar with, we cease to see. The writer shakes up the familiar scene, and, as if by magic, we see a new meaning in it."   Anaïs Nin

Writers' Voices invites you to discover new meaning. One way to discover new meaning is to learn something new. Another is to see in a new way something you already know.

Writers' Voices is a series of books. Each book contains selections from one or more writers' work. We chose the selections because the writers' voices can be clearly heard. Also, they deal with experiences that are interesting to think about and discuss.

If you are a new reader, you may want to have a selection read aloud to you, perhaps more than once. This will free you to enjoy the piece, to hear the language used, and to think about its meaning. Even if you are a more experienced reader, you may enjoy hearing the selection read aloud before reading it silently to yourself.

Each selection is set in a framework to expand your understanding of the selection. The framework includes a chapter that tells about the writer's life. Some authors write about their own lives; others write stories from their imagination. You may wonder why an author chose to write what he or she did. Sometimes you can find the answer by knowing about the author's life.

You may also find chapters about the characters, the plot, and when or where the story took place. These will help you begin thinking about the selection. They will also help you understand what may be unfamiliar to you.

We encourage you to read *actively*. An active reader does many things—while reading, and before and after reading—that help him or her better understand

and enjoy a book. Here are some suggestions of things you can do:

Before Reading

• Read the front and back covers of the book, and look at the cover illustration. Ask yourself what you expect the book to be about, based on this information.

• Think about why you want to read this book. What do you want to discover, and what questions do you hope will be answered?

• Look at the contents page. Decide which chapters you want to read and in what order you want to read them.

During Reading

• Try to stay with the rhythm of the language. If you find any words or sentences you don't understand, keep reading to see if the meaning becomes clear. If it doesn't, go back and reread the difficult part or discuss it with others.

• Try to put yourself into the story.

• Ask yourself questions as you read. For example: Do I believe this story or this character? Why?

After Reading

• Ask yourself if the story makes you see any of your own experiences in a new way.

• Ask yourself if the story has given you any new information.

• Keep a journal in which you can write down your thoughts about what you have read, and save new words you have learned.

• Look over the questions at the end of the book. They are meant to help you discover more about what you have read and how it relates to you—as a person, as a reader, and as a writer. Try those questions that seem most interesting to you.

• Talk about what you have read with other readers.

Good writing should make you think after you put the book down. Whether you are a beginning reader, a more experienced reader, or a teacher of reading, we encourage you to take time to think about these books and to discuss your thoughts with others. If you want to read more books by the author of the selections, you can go to your bookstore or library to find them.

When you are finished with the book, we hope you will write to our editors about your reactions. We want to know your thoughts about our books, and what they have meant to you.

A TIMELINE OF EVENTS

World History		Family History
Chinese immigration to the U.S. begins.	1849–1850	
	1860s	Maxine's grandfather works on the transcontinental railroad in the American West.
The Chinese emperor is overthrown and a new government is formed.	1911	
	1924	Maxine's father comes to the United States.
China is at war with Japan.	1937–1945	
	1940	Maxine's mother comes to the United States.
	1940	Maxine Hong is born in Stockton, California.
After Communist victory, The People's Republic of China is established.	1949	

MAPS OF PLACES MENTIONED IN THE SELECTIONS

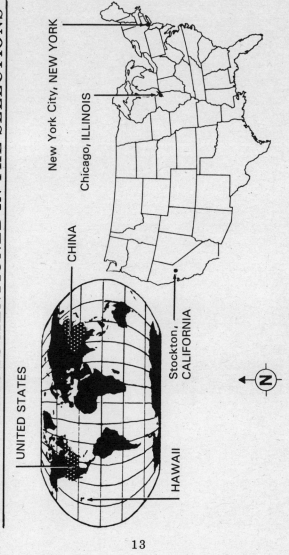

ABOUT
MAXINE HONG KINGSTON

Maxine Hong was born in Stockton,
California, on October 27, 1940. She grew
up in the Chinatown section of Stockton,
the oldest of six children. In the late
1950s and early 1960s, she studied
literature at the University of California
at Berkeley, where she met her husband,
Earll Kingston, who is an actor.

For many years, Maxine Hong Kingston and her husband lived in Honolulu,
Hawaii. To support herself while she
wrote books, she taught language and literature in high schools and colleges.
Maxine and Earll have one son, Joseph.
They now live in Oakland, California.

Kingston's cultural background has
been very important in her life and her
writing. Early in the 1800s, her great-
grandfather left China and went to
Hawaii to clear the land and plant
sugarcane for the big plantation owners.
In the 1860s, her grandfather came to the

American West to help build the railroad through the Sierra Nevada mountains. After working away from home for many years, both her great-grandfather and her grandfather returned to China.

In 1924, Kingston's father left China and traveled to New York City. Her mother followed in 1940. Her parents never returned to China.

Kingston has written two nonfiction books about her family and other Chinese Americans, *The Woman Warrior* and *China Men*. In addition to these two books, Maxine has written a novel called *Tripmaster Monkey*.

Although she was born in the United States, Kingston has always felt the strong influence of her Chinese heritage. She uses writing to help her understand her own life. In an interview in *Contemporary Authors*, she said, "Some of the things that happen to us in life seem to have no meaning, but when you write them down you find the meanings for them."

ABOUT
CHINESE IMMIGRATION
TO THE UNITED STATES

This chapter provides a short historical background for the selections.

In the early 1800s, people in China were suffering from floods, shortages of food, heavy taxes, and political oppression. Many decided to leave China in search of a better life.

Chinese pioneers—mostly men—first came to the United States to work as miners during the California gold rush. These men worked their own stakes; some also worked for American mining companies. By 1851, about 25,000 had arrived.

Later, the building of the railroads and the opening of the American West created a demand for manual laborers. The Central Pacific Railway Company alone hired over 12,000 Chinese men to build the railroad across the United States. They leveled the roadbeds, dug tunnels, and blasted away mountains.

Many other Chinese worked as farm laborers. By 1884, half the farm workers in California were Chinese. Others worked in the fishing industry or in light manufacturing jobs. Some Chinese found work as house servants and cooks and in laundries. By 1890, the census showed that 107,000 Chinese were in the United States.

Many Chinese men came to the United States as "sojourners" who stayed for several years and then returned to their families in China. These men called the United States the Gold Mountain. They told stories about gold nuggets lying in the streets and floating in the rivers.

In the 1880s, after the gold rush was over and the railroads were built, there was great unemployment in the United States. Some Americans blamed these troubles on the Chinese, who suffered many forms of persecution. They were attacked by mobs. New laws kept them from becoming U.S. citizens. Other laws prevented more Chinese men and women from immigrating to this country.

The Chinese pioneers felt strong pride in their heritage. Americans often found their ways to be strange and somewhat frightening. Chinese immigrants did not easily integrate into American society, nor were they welcomed by white Americans.

Large settlements, known as Chinatowns, grew up in many cities. In these small and crowded districts, the Chinese built temples and public halls, and opened stores, restaurants, laundries, and other businesses. Festivals and holidays were celebrated as they were in China.

The immigrants enjoyed Chinese opera and music. They played chess. Doctors and druggists sold traditional herbal remedies. Special organizations, called benevolent associations, helped new immigrants find housing and jobs.

Yet life in the old Chinatowns had negative aspects. One was overcrowding. Sometimes fifteen or twenty young men would share one small room. Another was the lack of women and families. Gambling and addiction to opium were also problems.

Many of the Chinese who came to this country kept strong ties to their native land. Even immigrants who made very low wages sent large portions of their paychecks back to their relatives in China year after year. Many Chinese who came to the U.S. planned to return someday to the town or village of their birth.

Starting in the 1930s and 1940s, the situation in China made it very difficult for Chinese Americans to think of returning to live there. A long war with Japan (1937–1945) and the establishment of the communist People's Republic of China (1949) made China a different country from the one they had left behind.

The American immigration laws were changed. In the 1940s, Chinese people again began to come to this country in large numbers. By 1980, the Chinese population was more than 806,000.

In the early days of Chinese immigration, most Chinese settled on the West Coast. Today more than half of the Chinese living in this country live in the Pacific Coast states. The San Francisco area has the largest population of Chinese. The New York City area is second, followed by Los Angeles and Honolulu.

While some Chinese Americans still live in Chinatowns, many others are integrated into other parts of American cities and towns. The descendants of the pioneering Chinese have grown up with a rich heritage. But they also find themselves to be part of two different worlds—one influenced by their Chinese history and the other shaped by their American past. Some have chosen to become completely Americanized, while others seek ways to unite the two parts into a new whole.

ABOUT THE SELECTION FROM
CHINA MEN

In *China Men,* Maxine Hong Kingston writes about her parents and grandparents and how they came to America.

In 1940, about 40,000 people lived in New York City's Chinatown. One of them was Maxine Hong Kingston's father. He lived in a laundry, which he owned with three other Chinese men. All four had given themselves new American names: Ed, Roosevelt, Woodrow, and Worldster.

Ed, Kingston's father, had left China and come to this country in 1924. This selection from *China Men* tells about his reunion with his wife in 1940.

Chinese Americans, like Ed, were always afraid that their citizenship papers would be questioned. It had been hard for Chinese living in the U.S. to become citizens. And there were still laws preventing new Chinese from coming to America. It was only because Ed was a citizen that it was possible for Kingston's mother to come legally.

Not only was it difficult to get into America, it was difficult to leave China. The Japanese army had invaded China, and Kingston's mother had to bribe people to get out. The ship almost didn't leave the harbor because of the fighting.

In this selection, Ed introduces his wife to the new ways of the United States. The story paints a vivid picture of what happens when old ways come face to face with new ways. In writing this account, Kingston relies on stories she has heard from her family, plus her own imagination.

You will read some special terms that the Chinese Americans used. They called the United States "the Gold Mountain," and they called non-Chinese people "demons" and "ghosts."

Perhaps the selection will make you think about what your parents' life might have been like before you were born. Perhaps it will remind you of a time when you found yourself in a strange new place.

CHINA MEN

Maxine Hong Kingston

IN THE SPRING, Ed sent his wife a picture of the four partners with their arms around one another's shoulders, laughing next to a Keep Off the Grass sign. He was wearing another two-hundred-dollar suit, a navy blue one, and a shirt with French cuffs, which closed with gold cuff links. For a winter picture, he sat on a rock in Central Park in his new gray greatcoat and jaunty hat and leather gloves lined with rabbit fur.

In his quiet time at night, he mounted the photographs in a fine leather album. With his first spending money, he had bought a postcard of the Statue of Liberty, the album, picture mounts, white ink, and a pen with a steel nib. He pasted that postcard in his expensive album, then added the other pictures.

Ed's wife wrote often and sometimes sent lichee, which she had picked from the three trees that Ed's father had planted and the twenty trees that Ed's brother had planted. When would he return to plant lichee trees?

Then she wrote that their two children had died. What should she do? "I think you ought to come back right now," she said.

He did much worrying, and hit upon a plan. He would not end his American life but show her how to live one. "Here's what you have to do if I'm to bring you to America," he wrote, though there was a law against her coming. "I will bring you to America on one condition, and that is, you get a Western education. I'll send you money, which you must only spend on school, not on food or clothes or jewelry or relatives. Leave the village. Go to Hong Kong or Canton and enroll in a Western scientific school. A science school. Get a degree. Send it to me as evidence you are educated, and I'll send you a ship ticket. And don't go to a school for classical literature. Go to a scientific school run by white people. And when you get your degree, I'll send for you to come here to the United States." He would figure out later how to accomplish that.

When next she wrote, she had enrolled in medical school; she was writing him from there. As years passed and sometimes she became discouraged with how long her education was taking and how difficult the work, he wrote encouragement: "If you don't get that degree, I'll not send for you. We will never see each other again." He did not want an ignorant villager for his American wife. . . .

At last she mailed him her diploma. He spent another few years saving passage money, and fifteen years after they had last seen one another, he sent for her. Applying for her, he risked having his citizenship again scrutinized. She would enter legally and gracefully, no question of asking a lady to ride the sea in a box or to swim to an unwatched shore.

At dinner one evening, he announced to his partners, "I've sent for my wife, who will be here in January." They were so surprised that they stopped their eating race.

"How did you save enough money?" Worldster asked.

"I guess you'll be moving to your own apartment," said Roosevelt.

"Why do you want to do that?" asked Woodrow.

After writing letters for fifteen years, Ed and his wife ended their correspondence. They were near each other, she on Ellis Island, where there was no mail, and he on Manhattan. When he saw her on the ferry, she was standing surrounded by bundles and bags, no child tugging her coat and no baby in her arms. He recognized her, though she was older. Her hair was slicked against her head with a bun in back, a proper married-lady hairdo. In spite of the law against her, she was landing, her papers in order. Her immigration verified the strength of his citizenship.

"Here you are," he said. "You've come."

"You look like a foreigner," she said. "I can barely recognize you."

"Was it a rough journey?" he asked.

"It was terrible," she exclaimed. "The Japanese were right behind me. When I tried to board the ship from Canton to Hong Kong, the man acted as if my papers were wrong and asked for a seventy-five-dollar bribe. So I ran to another gangplank and found out seventy-five dollars wasn't policy at all; this man wanted a hundred dollars. I had to run back to the first entrance. Then I paid another hundred to get off the ship. It was the last ship out of Canton before the Japanese took the harbor. And I was so seasick, I vomited the whole way across the Atlantic. And what a questioning I got on the Island. They asked me what year you had cut your queue, and a workman shook his head, hawked, and spat. It was a signal. So I said, 'I don't know.' On my way to be locked up again, I said to that workman, 'That was a delicious bun you gave me. Thank you. I hope you bring me another if you have more.' Get it? It was a code I made up, meaning, 'Thank you for giving me the right answer. Please give me more help.' Oh, I was so scared. If it weren't for him I might not be here."

"Don't worry any more," said Ed. "That's over now. Don't worry any more." Her big eyes had lines around them. "That's all over now," he said.

"I had to build roads," she said. "Since your father is too crazy to work, and you were away, I had to pay the labor tax for two men. Your father followed me and wept on the road when I left."

"Never mind now," he said. "That's all over now."

They rode the subway to the room he had rented in preparation for her coming. He taught her the name of the subway stop for the laundry. "Easu Bu-odd-way Su-ta-son," she repeated. "That's good," he said. "Remember that, and you can't get lost."

She unpacked jars of seeds. "But we aren't farmers any more," he said. "I'll plant in tin cans and put them out here on the fire escape," she said. "You'll see how many vegetables we can grow in cans."

She showed him a piece of cloth. "Do you recognize this?" she asked. "The Japanese were right behind me, and I had time to take just one keepsake—the trimming on the bed canopy." She had ripped it off and shoved it in her purse. She unfolded it. "This is the only thing we have left from China," she said. "The heirloom." A red phoenix and a red dragon played across the strip of linen; the Chinese words down one end and English words across the top said, "Good morning." She had cross-stitched it herself.

"You could write English even then," he teased her, "and getting ready to come here." "I didn't know what it said," she demurred, "I only copied it from a needlework book."

He took her shopping and bought her a

black crepe dress with a bodice of white lace ruffles and buttons of rhinestone and silver. "You look very pretty," he told her. They bought a black coat with a fur collar and a little black-eyed animal head over her shoulder, high heels, silk stockings, black kid gloves, and a picture hat with a wide, wide brim and silk fluttery ribbon. They strolled in their finery along Fifth Avenue. "I washed all these windows," he told her. "When I first came here, I borrowed a squeegee and rags and a bucket, and walked up and down this street. I went inside each store and asked if they wanted the windows washed. The white foreigners aren't so hard to get along with; they nod to mean Yes and shake their heads to mean No, the same as anybody." New York glittered and shined with glass. He had liked pulling the water off the panes and leaving brief rainbows. While working, he had looked over the displays of all the wonderful clothes to own and wear. He had made the money to pool for starting the laundry.

"In the spring," he promised her, "we'll buy you white cotton gloves."

"On the first day of autumn," he told her, "New Yorkers stomp on one another's straw hats. I wear my gray felt one as soon as summer's over. I save the straw for spring. I'm not extravagant. You ought to put your earrings in the safe deposit box at the bank. Pierced ears look a little primitive in this country." He also told her to buy makeup at a drugstore. "American people don't like oily faces. So you ought to use some powder. It's the custom. Also buy some rouge. These foreigners dislike yellow skin."

She also bought a long black rat of hair to roll her own hair over for an upswept hairdo. At a beauty parlor, she had her wavy hair cut and curled tighter with a marcel. She washed, ironed, and wrapped her silk pants and dresses and never wore them again.

He took her to see the Statue of Liberty. They climbed the ladder, she in high heels, up the arm to the torch, then the stairs to the crown. "Now we're inside her chin. This part must be the nose." From the windows of the crown, he showed her his city.

They also went to the top of the Empire State Building, took the second elevator to the very top, the top of the world. Ed loved the way he could look up at the uncluttered sky. They put money in the telescopes and looked for the laundry and their apartment. "So I have been on the tallest building in the world," she said. "I have seen everything. Wonderful. Wonderful. Amazing. Amazing."

"Yes," he said. "Everything's possible on the Gold Mountain. I've danced with blondes." "No, really?" she said. "You didn't. You're making that up, aren't you? You danced with demonesses? I don't believe it."

Her favorite place to go was the free aquarium, "the fish house," where all manner of creatures swam. Walking between the lighted tanks, she asked, "When do you think we'll go back to China? Do you think we'll go back to China?" "Shh," he said. "Shh." The electric eels glowed in their dark tank, and the talking fish made noises. "There are bigger fish in China," she said.

They went to the movies and saw *Young Tom Edison* with Mickey Rooney. They both liked the scene where the mother took Eh-Da-Son into the barn, but only pretended to thrash him; she faked the slaps and crying and scolding to fool the strict father, the father "the severe parent," according to Confucius, and the mother "the kind parent.". . . After the movie, Ed explained to his wife that this cunning, resourceful, successful inventor, Edison, was who he had named himself after. "I see," she said. "Eh-Da-Son. Son as in *sage* or *immortal* or *saint.*". . .

The four partners no longer had to race to get out of doing the dishes. Ed's wife shopped and cooked. She bought a tiered food carrier, filled each pot with a different accompaniment to rice, and carried it and a pot of soup hot through the subway to the laundry. The first day she did this, she got off at the wrong stop in the underground city. She went from white ghost to white ghost shouting over the trains, which sounded like the Japanese bombing, "Easu Bu-odd-way Su-ta-son?" And a conductor said, "Of course. East Broadway Station. Go that way."

"He understood me," she proudly told the men. "I can speak English very well." She set the table with her homemade meal so they didn't get to buy restaurant take-out food any more. And they did not race but had manners. "Tell me how you started this laundry," she said. Woodrow described their Grand Opening. "Our friends sent stands of flowers tied in wide red ribbons, on which your husband wrote good words in gold ink. We exploded firecrackers out on the sidewalk, right out there on Mott Street. And then the customers came." "Working for ourselves, we can close whenever we please and go do as we like," Ed said.

The partners did not tell her that they hardly ever celebrated holidays. . . . If they did not go to the bother of keeping it, a holiday was another free day. It was that free a country. They could neglect attending the big public celebrations such as those at the benevolent associations and New Year's eve at Times Square, and no one minded. Neglecting the planting and harvest days made no difference in New York. No neighbors looked askance. And there were no godly repercussions. They had no graves to decorate for the memorial days of Clarity and Brightness. They did arrange cotton snow, reindeer, a stable scene, and a Santa Claus in the laundry window at Christmas. "We don't want them to break our window or not bring their laundry," Ed explained. His wife brought back the holidays. She made the holidays appear again.

Her arrival ended Ed's independent life. She stopped him from reading while eating. She'd learned at the school of Western medicine, she said, that doing those two actions at once divides the available blood between brain and stomach; one should concentrate. She kept telling

Ed to cut down on his smoking. She polished his World's Fair copper souvenir ashtray clean. She cut new covers from brown wrapping paper and shirt cardboards for his books, and resewed the bindings. He inked the new covers with the titles, authors, and volume numbers.

When the partners took the couple to a restaurant, the men wiped their chopsticks and bowls with napkins. "That doesn't really clean them, you know," she said. "All you're doing is wiping the germs around. Germs are little animals invisible to the naked eye." "That must be a superstition from your village, a village superstition," said Worldster. "You ought to give up village superstitions in America." The next day she brought her microscope to the laundry and showed them the germs under their fingernails and on their tongues and in the water.

At one of their dinners, Worldster handed papers to Woodrow and Roosevelt, and the three of them started discussing business.

"What is this?" said Ed.

"Deeds for the business," said Worldster, "contracts for the partnership."

"Where's mine?" said Ed. "What contracts? Why contracts all of a sudden?"

"Where's his?" asked his wife.

"You weren't at the meeting," said Worldster.

"Since when did we have to have contracts?" Ed asked. "We had a spoken partnership. We shook hands. We gave one another our word."

"We wrote it down too," said Worldster. "I guess you have the status of an employee."

"I don't see why you didn't show up for the meeting," said Roosevelt.

"This is all perfectly legal," said Woodrow. "Look—registered with the demon courts." It was in English. There wasn't anything Ed could do. They had ganged up on him and swindled him out of his share of the laundry. "You were always reading when we were working," somebody said.

"What are we going to do?" said his wife, the lines around her eyes and mouth deepening.

"Don't worry," he said. "I've been planning for us to go to California anyway."

So the two of them took a train across the United States, stopping in Chicago to visit some relatives—they saw more of the United States than they had ever seen of China—and went to live in California, which some say is the real Gold Mountain anyway.

ABOUT THE SELECTION FROM
THE WOMAN WARRIOR

In *The Woman Warrior,* Maxine Hong
Kingston remembers growing up. Her
parents, who had come to this country
from China, kept the old Chinese ways.
Kingston was born here, but she felt nei-
ther completely Chinese nor completely
American. In *The Woman Warrior,* she
tries to unite her past and her present.

The following selection from *The
Woman Warrior* takes place some thirty
years after Kingston's mother came to
New York. In this selection, Maxine is a
grown-up woman. She has come home for
a visit to her parents, to the house in
Stockton, California, where she grew up.

In the selection from *China Men,*
Kingston told how her mother came to this
country to be with her husband. How-
ever, in that story she didn't refer to her
parents as "my mother" and "my father." She didn't bring herself into the

story at all. She wrote about her parents as "he" and "she."

Now, in this selection from *The Woman Warrior,* Kingston herself is part of the story. She talks about her mother, but she also talks with her mother. Maxine is in this story, speaking to the reader as "I." She explains her feelings directly and very personally.

Maxine is trying to sleep, but her mother wants to talk. As the two women speak, we learn how Maxine sees her mother and how she feels about her.

The old woman is funny, difficult, and demanding. As Maxine says, "All her children gnash their teeth." Facts don't always stack up right when her mother talks. Also, she complains about working too hard, but won't think of stopping, even though she is more than seventy years old.

Although thirty years have passed since she came to the United States, Maxine's mother still refers to non-Chinese people as "ghosts." She tells Maxine,

"You're always listening to Teacher Ghosts, those Scientist Ghosts, Doctor Ghosts." She doesn't mean that they are dead, just that they are not Chinese.

Memories of life in China are very strong for Maxine's mother, as are memories of the long years of working in the laundry that she and her husband owned in Stockton.

While she loves her mother and tries to understand her, Maxine also feels frustrated in dealing with her old-fashioned and strange ways. Despite their differences, we can feel the affection that this mother and daughter have for one another.

At the end of this selection, Maxine's mother calls her "Little Dog," a special nickname. In Chinese astrology, some years are the Year of the Dog, some are the Year of the Dragon, and so on. Maxine and her mother were both born in Dragon years. But, superstitiously, her mother tries to fool the gods by pretending Maxine was born under the Dog sign.

Perhaps the selection will make you

think about a frustrating conversation you have had with one of your parents or another older person. Perhaps it will remind you of a visit to the place where you grew up, or your memories of that place.

THE WOMAN WARRIOR

Maxine Hong Kingston

WHEN I LAST VISITED my parents, I had trouble falling asleep, too big for the hills and valleys scooped in the mattress by child-bodies. I heard my mother come in. I stopped moving. What did she want? Eyes shut, I pictured my mother, her white hair frizzy in the dark-and-light doorway, my hair white now too, Mother. I could hear her move furniture about. Then she dragged a third quilt, the thick, homemade Chinese kind, across me. After that I lost track of her location. I spied from beneath my eyelids and had to hold back a jump. She had pulled up a chair and was sitting by the bed next to my head. I could see her strong hands in her lap, not working fourteen pairs of needles.

She is very proud of her hands, which can make anything and stay pink and soft while my father's became like carved wood. Her palm lines do not branch into head, heart, and life lines like other people's but crease with just one atavistic fold. That night she was a sad bear; a great sheep in a wool shawl. She recently took to wearing shawls and granny glasses, American fashions. What did she want, sitting there so large next to my head? I could feel her stare—her eyes two lights warm on my graying hair, then on the creases at the sides of my mouth, my thin neck, my thin cheeks, my thin arms. I felt her sight warm each of my bony elbows, and I flopped about in my fake sleep to hide them from her criticism. She sent light at full brightness beaming through my eyelids, her eyes at my eyes, and I had to open them.

"What's the matter, Mama? Why are you sitting there?"

She reached over and switched on a lamp she had placed on the floor beside her. "I swallowed that LSD pill you left on the kitchen counter," she announced.

"That wasn't LSD, Mama. It was just a cold pill. I have a cold."

"You're always catching colds when you come home. You must be eating too much *yin.* Let me get you another quilt."

"No, no more quilts. You shouldn't take pills that aren't prescribed for you. 'Don't eat pills you find on the curb,' you always told us."

"You children never tell me what you're really up to. How else am I going to find out what you're really up to?" As if her head hurt, she closed her eyes behind the gold wire rims. "Aiaa," she sighed, "how can I bear to have you leave me again?"

How can I bear to leave her again? She would close up this room, open temporarily for me, and wander about cleaning and cleaning the shrunken house, so tidy since our leaving. . . .

The lamp gave off the sort of light that comes from a television, which made the high ceiling disappear and then suddenly drop back into place. I could feel that clamping down and see how my mother had pulled the blinds down so low that the bare rollers were showing. No passer-by would detect a daughter in this house. My mother would sometimes be a large animal, barely real in the dark; then she would become a mother again. I could see the wrinkles around her big eyes, and I could see her cheeks sunken without her top teeth.

"I'll be back again soon," I said. "You know that I come back. I think of you when I'm not here."

"Yes, I know you. I know you now. I've always known you. You're the one with the charming words. You have never come back. 'I'll be back on Turkeyday,' you said. Huh."

I shut my teeth together, vocal cords cut, they hurt so. I would not speak words to give her pain. All her children gnash their teeth.

"The last time I saw you, you were still young," she said. "Now you're old."

"It's only been a year since I visited you."

"That's the year you turned old. Look at you, hair gone gray, and you haven't even fattened up yet. I know how the Chinese talk about us. 'They're so poor,' they say, 'they can't afford to fatten up any of their daughters.' 'Years in America,' they say, 'and they don't eat.' Oh, the shame of it—a whole family of skinny children. And your father—he's so skinny, he's disappearing."

"Don't worry about him, Mama. Doctors are saying that skinny people live longer. Papa's going to live a long time."

"So! I knew I didn't have too many years left. Do you know how I got all this fat? Eating your leftovers. Aiaa, I'm getting so old. Soon you will have no more mother."

"Mama, you've been saying that all my life."

"This time it's true. I'm almost eighty."

"I thought you were only seventy-six."

"My papers are wrong. I'm eighty."

"But I thought your papers are wrong, and you're seventy-two, seventy-three in Chinese years."

"My papers are wrong, and I'm eighty, eighty-one in Chinese years. Seventy. Eighty. What do numbers matter? I'm dropping dead any day now. The aunt down the street was resting on her porch steps, dinner all cooked, waiting for her husband and son to come home and eat it. She closed her eyes for a moment and died. Isn't that a wonderful way to go?"

"But our family lives to be ninety-nine."

"That's your father's family. My mother and father died very young. My youngest sister was an orphan at ten. Our parents were not even fifty."

"Then you should feel grateful you've lived so many extra years."

"I was so sure you were going to be an orphan too. In fact, I'm amazed you've lived to have white hair. Why don't you dye it?"

"Hair color doesn't measure age,

Mother. White is just another pigment, like black and brown."

"You're always listening to Teacher Ghosts, those Scientist Ghosts, Doctor Ghosts."

"I have to make a living.". . .

She leaned forward, eyes brimming with what she was about to say: "I work so hard," she said. She was doing her stare—at what? My feet began rubbing together as if to tear each other's skin off. She started talking again, "The tomato vines prickle my hands; I can feel their little stubble hairs right through my gloves. My feet squish-squish in the rotten tomatoes, squish-squish in the tomato mud the feet ahead of me have sucked. And do you know the best way to stop the itch from the tomato hairs? You break open a fresh tomato and wash yourself with it. You cool your face in tomato juice. Oh, but it's the potatoes that will ruin my hands. I'll get rheumatism washing potatoes, squatting over potatoes."

She had taken off the Ace bandages

around her legs for the night. The varicose veins stood out.

"Mama, why don't you stop working? You don't have to work anymore. Do you? Do you really have to work like that? Scabbing in the tomato fields?" Her black hair seems filleted with the band of white at its roots. She dyed her hair so that the farmers would hire her. She would walk to Skid Row and stand in line with the hobos, the winos, the junkies, and the Mexicans until the farm buses came and the farmers picked out the workers they wanted. "You have the house," I said. "For food you have Social Security. And urban renewal must have given you something. It was good in a way when they tore down the laundry. Really, Mama, it was. Otherwise Papa would never have retired. You ought to retire too."

"Do you think your father wanted to stop work? Look at his eyes; the brown is going out of his eyes. He has stopped talking. When I go to work, he eats leftovers. He doesn't cook new food," she said, confessing, me maddened at confessions. "Those Urban Renewal Ghosts gave us moving money. It took us seventeen years to get our customers. How could we start all over on moving money, as if we two old people had another seventeen years in us? Aa"—she flipped something aside with her hand—"White Ghosts can't tell Chinese age."

I closed my eyes and breathed evenly, but she could tell I wasn't asleep.

"This is terrible ghost country, where a human being works her life away," she said. "Even the ghosts work, no time for acrobatics. I have not stopped working since the day the ship landed. I was on my feet the moment the babies were out. In China I never even had to hang up my own clothes. I shouldn't have left, but your father couldn't have supported you without me. I'm the one with the big muscles."

"If you hadn't left, there wouldn't have been a me for you two to support. Mama,

I'm really sleepy. Do you mind letting me sleep?" I do not believe in old age. I do not believe in getting tired.

"I didn't need muscles in China. I was small in China." She was. The silk dresses she gave me are tiny. You would not think the same person wore them. This mother can carry a hundred pounds of Texas rice up- and downstairs. She could work at the laundry from 6:30 a.m. until midnight, shifting a baby from an ironing table to a shelf between packages, to the display window, where the ghosts tapped on the glass. "I put you babies in the clean places at the laundry, as far away from the germs that fumed out of the ghosts' clothes as I could. Aa, their socks and handkerchiefs choked me. I cough now because of those seventeen years of breathing dust. Tubercular handkerchiefs. Lepers' socks." I thought she had wanted to show off my baby sister in the display window.

In the midnight unsteadiness we were back at the laundry, and my mother was sitting on an orange crate sorting dirty clothes into mountains—a sheet mountain, a white shirt mountain, a dark shirt mountain, a work-pants mountain, a long underwear mountain, a short underwear mountain, a little hill of socks pinned together in pairs, a little hill of handkerchiefs pinned to tags. Surrounding her were candles she burned in daylight, clean yellow diamonds, footlights that ringed her, mysterious masked mother, nose and mouth veiled with a cowboy handkerchief. Before undoing the bundles, my mother would light a tall new candle, which was a luxury, and the pie pans full of old wax and wicks that sometimes sputtered blue, a noise I thought was the germs getting seared.

"No tickee, no washee, mama-san?" a ghost would say, so embarrassing.

"Noisy Red-Mouth Ghost," she'd write on its package, naming it, marking its clothes with its name.

Back in the bedroom I said, "The candles must have helped. It was a good idea of yours to use candles."

"They didn't do much good. All I have

to do is think about dust sifting out of clothes or peat dirt blowing across a field or chick mash falling from a scoop, and I start coughing." She coughed deeply. "See what I mean? I have worked too much. Human beings don't work like this in China. Time goes slower there. Here we have to hurry, feed the hungry children before we're too old to work. I feel like a mother cat hunting for its kittens. She has to find them fast because in a few hours she will forget how to count or that she had any kittens at all. I can't sleep in this country because it doesn't shut down for the night. Factories, canneries, restaurants—always somebody somewhere working through the night. It never gets done all at once here. Time was different in China. One year lasted as long as my total time here; one evening so long, you could visit your women friends, drink tea, and play cards at each house, and it would still be twilight. It even got boring, nothing to do but fan ourselves. Here midnight comes and the floor's not swept, the ironing's not ready, the money's not made. I would still be young if we lived in China."

. . .

"There's only one thing that I really want anymore. I want you here, not wandering like a ghost from Romany. I want every one of you living here together. When you're all home, all six of you with your children and husbands and wives, there are twenty or thirty people in this house. Then I'm happy. And your father is happy. Whichever room I walk into overflows with my relatives, grandsons, sons-in-law. I can't turn around without touching somebody. That's the way a house should be." Her eyes are big, inconsolable. A spider headache spreads out in fine branches over my skull. She is etching spider legs into the icy bone. She pries open my head and my fists and crams into them responsibility for time, responsibility for intervening oceans.

The gods pay her and my father back for leaving their parents. My grandmother wrote letters pleading for them to come home, and they ignored her. Now they know how she felt.

"When I'm away from here," I had to tell her, "I don't get sick. I don't go to the hospital every holiday. I don't get pneumonia, no dark spots on my x-rays. My chest doesn't hurt when I breathe. I can breathe. And I don't get headaches at 3:00. I don't have to take medicines or go to doctors. Elsewhere I don't have to lock my doors and keep checking the locks. I don't stand at the windows and watch for movements and see them in the dark."

"What do you mean you don't lock your doors?"

"I do. I do. But not the way I do here. I don't hear ghost sounds. I don't stay awake listening to walking in the kitchen. I don't hear the doors and windows unhinging."

"It was probably just a Wino Ghost or a Hobo Ghost looking for a place to sleep."

"I don't want to hear Wino Ghosts and

Hobo Ghosts. I've found some places in this country that are ghost-free. And I think I belong there, where I don't catch colds or use my hospitalization insurance. Here I'm sick so often, I can barely work. I can't help it, Mama."

She yawned. "It's better, then, for you to stay away. The weather in California must not agree with you. You can come for visits." She got up and turned off the light. "Of course, you must go, Little Dog."

A weight lifted from me. The quilts must be filling with air. The world is somehow lighter. She has not called me that endearment for years—a name to fool the gods. I am really a Dragon, as she is a Dragon, both of us born in dragon years. I am practically a first daughter of a first daughter.

"Good night, Little Dog."

"Good night, Mother."

GLOSSARY

Demons, demonesses. Terms the Chinese immigrants used to describe non-Chinese people.

Ellis Island. A small island near New York City where many new immigrants were held, while waiting for permission to enter America.

Ghosts. A term the Chinese immigrants used to describe non-Chinese people.

Gold Mountain. A name the Chinese used for the United States.

Lichee. The fruit of a tree that grows in China.

Queue. The braid that Chinese peasant men wore; it showed loyalty to the Manchu emperor. Many men cut off their queues in 1911, to show they supported the new republican government.

Yin. One of the two basic elements in the universe, according to the Chinese. It represents all that is dark, cold, wet, and sweet. The other basic element is *yang*, representing all that is light, hot, dry, and tart.

QUESTIONS FOR THE READER

Thinking about the Story

1. What did you think about the selections from *China Men* and *The Woman Warrior*? What did you like or not like?

2. Are there ways that the events or people in the selections became important or special to you? Write about or discuss these.

3. What do you think were the most important things Maxine Hong Kingston wanted to say in the selections?

4. In what ways did the selections answer the questions you had before you began reading or listening?

5. Were any parts of the selections difficult to understand? If so, you may want to read or listen to them again. You might think about why they were difficult.

Thinking about the Writing

1. How did Maxine Hong Kingston help you see, hear, and feel what happened in the se-

lections? Find the words, phrases, or sentences that did this best.

2. Writers think carefully about their stories' settings, characters, and events. In writing these selections, which of these things do you think Maxine Hong Kingston felt was most important? Find the parts of the story that support your opinion.

3. Which character in each selection was most interesting to you? How did Maxine Hong Kingston help you learn about this person? Find the places in each selection where you learned the most about this person.

4. In each selection, Maxine Hong Kingston uses dialogue. Dialogue can make a story stronger and more alive. Pick out some dialogue that you feel is strong, and explain how it helps the story.

5. The selection from *China Men* is written from the point of view of someone outside the story who tells us what is happening. The writer uses the words "he" and "she." The selection from *The Woman Warrior* is seen through the writer's eyes. She uses the words

"I" and "me." What difference does this create in the writing of the two selections?

6. Maxine Hong Kingston, through her writing, makes us understand some of the unique things about Chinese culture. Find some parts in the selections that helped you understand this culture.

Activities

1. Were there any words that were difficult for you in the selections from *China Men* and *The Woman Warrior*? Go back to these words and try to figure out their meanings. Discuss what you think each word means, and why you made that guess. Discuss with your teacher or another student how you are going to remember each word. Some ways to remember words are to put them on file cards, or write them in your journal, or create a personal dictionary. Be sure to use the words in your writing in a way that will help you to remember their meaning.

2. How did you help yourself understand the selections? Did you ask yourself questions? What were they? Discuss these questions

with other people who have read the same selections, or write about them in your journal.

3. Talking with other people about what you have read can increase your understanding of it. Discussion can help you organize your thoughts, get new ideas, and rethink your original ideas. Discuss your thoughts about the selections with someone else who has read them. Find out if your opinions are the same or different. See if your thoughts change as a result of this discussion.

4. After you finish reading or listening, you might want to write down your thoughts about the book. You could write a book review, or a letter to a friend you think might be interested in the book. You could write your reflections on the book in your journal, or you could write about topics the book has brought up that you want to explore further.

5. Did reading the selections give you any ideas for your own writing? You might want to write about:

• some part of your family history.

• your relationship with a parent or older person.

• a time you were in a strange new place.

6. Sometimes organizing information in a visual way can help you better understand or remember it. Look at the timeline of world history and Maxine Hong Kingston's family's history. You might want to make a similar timeline for your family.

7. You might interview some people who come from backgrounds or cultures different from your own. Make a list of questions to ask. Afterwards, discuss what you learn from these oral histories.

8. Think about a strong person you have known who has influenced you in some way. Why was this person important to you? You might want to write about this person, or write a letter to him or her.

9. If you could talk to Maxine Hong Kingston, what questions would you ask about her writing? You might want to write the questions in your journal.